JANE EYRE

**A GRAPHIC CLASSIC BY
TRINA ROBBINS**

**BASED ON THE NOVEL BY
CHARLOTTE BRONTË**

SCHOLASTIC INC.
New York Toronto London Auckland Sydney
Mexico City New Delhi Hong Kong Buenos Aires

PENCILLER
MICHAEL LILLY

INKER
SCOTT GOODELL

COLORIST
MICHELLE WULFSON

LETTERER
JON OOSTING

COVER ARTIST
MICHAEL LILLY

COVER COLORS
J. BROWN AND TECH FX

Copyright © 1999 by Scholastic Inc.
All rights reserved. Published by Scholastic Inc.
Printed in the U.S.A.

ISBN 0-439-12377-1
(meets NASTA specifications)

SCHOLASTIC, READ 180, and associated logos and designs are trademarks and/or registered trademarks of Scholastic Inc.

LEXILE is a registered trademark of MetaMetrics, Inc.

4 5 6 7 8 9 10   23   12 11 10 09 08 07

JANE EYRE

CHARLOTTE BRONTË'S CHILDHOOD WAS A NIGHTMARE. WHEN SHE WAS VERY YOUNG, HER MOTHER DIED.

HER FATHER THEN SENT HER AND HER SISTERS TO BOARDING SCHOOL. THERE, THE CONDITIONS WERE SO TERRIBLE THAT TWO BRONTË SISTERS DIED. CHARLOTTE RETURNED HOME LONELY AND HEARTBROKEN.

CHARLOTTE AND HER REMAINING SISTERS, EMILY AND ANN, BEGAN TO WRITE STORIES, PLAYS, AND EVEN SMALL BOOKS IN THEIR FREE TIME. AT FIRST THEY WROTE ABOUT IMAGINARY LANDS. LATER THEY DESCRIBED THEIR OWN EXPERIENCES.

CHARLOTTE'S NOVEL ABOUT A BRAVE ORPHAN GIRL, JANE EYRE, WAS BASED PARTLY ON HER OWN CHILDHOOD. PUBLISHED IN ENGLAND IN 1847, JANE EYRE BECAME AN IMMEDIATE BEST-SELLER.

MY PARENTS DIED WHEN I WAS A BABY. I WAS TAKEN IN BY MY AUNT, MRS. REED.

Go on, Jane. Your aunt wants to see you.

ENTER!

MRS. REED NEVER LET ME FORGET THAT I WAS A POOR RELATIVE.

Is this the naughty little girl you were telling me about, Mrs. Reed?

4

I know Mr. Brocklehurst was wrong. My name is Helen. *(cough! cough!)*

MY BEST FRIEND, HELEN, WAS WEAK AND SICK.

CONDITIONS AT LOWOOD WERE HARSH. THE FOOD WAS TERRIBLE ...

Ugh! The cereal is burned again!

... AND THE BUILDING WAS COLD AND DRAFTY.

Disgraceful! Your hands are dirty!

That isn't fair. Helen couldn't wash this morning, because the water was frozen.

HELEN GOT SICKER AND SICKER.

INFIRMARY

I'm afraid Helen will not be with us much longer.

Oh no! You mean she's going to die?!

LATE ONE NIGHT ...

Ssh! Helen, I had to see you. I was afraid for you.

Don't be afraid. I'm not in pain, but I am so tired. Don't leave me.

I'll stay with you, dear Helen. No one shall take me away.

I MUST HAVE FALLEN ASLEEP DURING THE NIGHT. WHEN I AWOKE IT WAS MORNING.

Helen? Helen!!

Poor child. Your friend is dead.

Oh, Helen! *(sob)* Helen! *(sob)*

THE NEXT DAY, MY NEW LIFE BEGAN.

This is Adele, your new student.

Hello, Mademoiselle! Will you teach me English?

She's French!

Yes, the master adopted her in Paris.

Will I meet Mr. Rochester today?

Mr. Rochester is not here. He travels a great deal, and we never know when he will return.

I WAS HAPPY AT THORNFIELD. MRS. FAIRFAX WAS KIND TO ME, AND I LOVED LITTLE ADELE. BUT I WONDERED WHEN I WOULD MEET MR. ROCHESTER AND WHAT HE WOULD BE LIKE.

WHEN I RETURNED ...

Pilot!

Miss Eyre! The master has returned, and he wants to see you in the library!

So this is Jane. Sit.

Mademoiselle, see what Mr. Rochester brought me!

Well, Jane, are you happy here at Thornfield?

Yes, sir.

Do you have a family? Parents?

No, sir. I am an orphan.

And where did you go to school, Jane?

I went to Lowood Institution for Orphans, sir.

I've heard of Lowood. Mr. Brocklehurst is the director there. Doubtless you all adored him.

No sir. I disliked him, and I was not alone.

He is a harsh man. He starved us and bored us with his long lectures.

What did you think of Mr. Rochester?

He is very moody and not very polite.

I'm afraid that's because he's unhappy.

Well! You certainly are honest!

Enough of this talking. It's past Adele's bedtime. Put her to bed!

WHEN I NEXT SAW MR. ROCHESTER, HE WAS IN A BETTER MOOD.

Ah, Jane! Let's go for a walk!

If you like, sir.

Then she ran off, abandoning her daughter. The poor child had no one to care for her, so I adopted her.

Perhaps you have wondered about Adele. Her mother was a beautiful widow—a ballet dancer in France.

I was in love with her, and I thought that she loved me, too.

So, he is not as gruff as he pretends!

ONCE I REALIZED MR. ROCHESTER WAS ACTUALLY A GOOD PERSON, I FELT THAT MY LIFE AT THORNFIELD WAS PERFECT. BUT THEN, ONE NIGHT ...

HA! HA! HAAAA!

That strange laughter again!

Who is there?

That's odd. The hall is empty.

Smoke! There's a fire in Mr. Rochester's room!

(splutter) Jane! Are you trying to drown me?

Wake up, sir! Your bed is on fire!

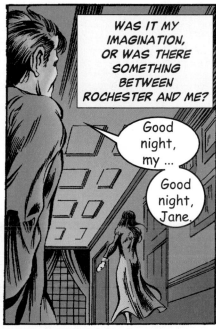

Jane, the master wants you to come down with Adele.

Oh, I'm sure he just wants to see Adele.

He insists that you come, too.

And here is my adopted daughter, Adele.

What a little monkey! I didn't know you liked children, Edward.

I don't. But her mother abandoned her, and I couldn't just leave her all alone.

Hmmph! The child should be sent away to boarding school.

I have hired a governess to teach Adele.

Oh, that plain creature over there. I *detest* governesses!

19

He'll marry Blanche. Then Adele will go to boarding school, and I'll be sent away!

Jane!

Jane, you look unhappy! Is it because I will soon be married, and you will have to leave Thornfield?

(sniff!) Yes, sir.

I will never see you again, but, of course, you will forget me.

I will never forget you! (sob!) Do you think that because I am—*sob*—poor and plain, that I have no heart?

I have more heart than you, for I don't believe you really love Miss Ingram!

FINALLY, THE DAY ARRIVED.

If anyone knows any reason why these two may not marry ...

STOP!

SUDDENLY ...

Edward Rochester cannot marry this woman!

He is still married to my sister, Bertha, who lives at Thornfield!

Edward ... ?

Yes, he speaks the truth. Come, I will show you.

I WAS TAKEN IN BY A KIND FAMILY. FOR DAYS I LAY ILL.

How can I thank ... ?

Ssh! You must rest.

SLOWLY MY BODY HEALED.

BUT MY HEART DID NOT HEAL.

Oh, Edward! What has happened to you?

SUDDENLY ...

Jane! Jane! Jane!

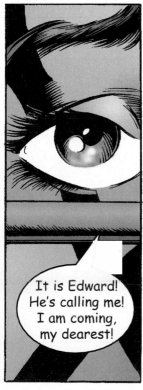

It is Edward! He's calling me! I am coming, my dearest!

BUT WHEN I ARRIVED BACK AT THORNFIELD ...

It is a burned-out ruin!

A week after you left, Mr. Rochester's wife escaped and set fire to the house. He rescued Adele.

"THEN MR. ROCHESTER SAW HIS WIFE STANDING ON THE ROOF, SURROUNDED BY FLAMES. HE TRIED TO SAVE HER."

Take my hand!

HA HA HAAAA!

But she jumped from the roof to her death, and the master was blinded by the fire.

He sits inside now and never goes out.

I must go to him.

WOOF! WOOF!

Who is that with you, Pilot? Is it a stranger?